Jub

ORANGE
silver
S A U S A G E

First published 2009 by Walker Books Ltd
87 Vauxhall Walk, London SE11 5HJ

2 4 6 8 10 9 7 5 3

This book has been typeset in Futura

Printed in Great Britain by Clays Ltd, St Ives plc

British Library Cataloguing in Publication Data:
a catalogue record for this book is available from the British Library

ISBN 978-1-4063-1701-5

www.walker.co.uk

WALKER BOOKS
AND SUBSIDIARIES
LONDON · BOSTON · SYDNEY · AUCKLAND

ORANGE
silver
SAUSAGE

a collection of
POEMS WITHOUT RHYMES

from Zephaniah To Agard

COMPILED BY JAMES CARTER & GRAHAM DENTON
ILLUSTRATED BY SALVATORE RUBBINO

Contents

For someone who rarely rhymes
but is always awesome, with warmest
thanks to Jacqueline Wilson.
J.C.

For Robert Scotellaro,
my friend across the pond.
G.D.

Introduction

Poems *without* rhymes? Are you kidding? That's what poems are, aren't they – things that rhyme? It can certainly seem like it. From birth onwards you are given all kinds of rhyming stuff – nursery rhymes, lullabies, nonsense rhymes and limericks. Then, when you get to about the age of eight, a teacher will tell you that, no, not all poems do rhyme. What are you meant to think? But it's true. There are literally thousands of poems that don't rhyme. Most modern poets write both rhyming and non-rhyming poems – and some don't use rhyme at all. Read this book and you'll find classic and contemporary poems in an array of voices, styles and tones, on a wide range of subjects – and NONE of them rhymes.

Then, if you want to write your own non-rhyming poems and need a few pointers to get you going, turn to the section at the back of the book.

And, if you're wondering why *Orange Silver Sausage*, these three words are the title of a poem by Colin West, who had a bit of a problem:

> *Some words I've studied for a time,*
> *Like orange, silver, sausage;*
> *But as for finding them a rhyme,*
> *I'm at a total lossage.*

Thank you for our title, Colin!

7

G r e e t

Assalaam Alaikum

Hola

Szia

Sat Srii Akaal

Wa Happen

Zdravo

Yia Sou

Merhaba

Hej

Yo

Sawast Dee Craap

Ciao

Zdravstvuyte

Endemenesh

Ahoj

8

T i n g s

Bonjour

Yassou

Shalom

Namaste

Dag

Guten Tag

Buenos Dias

Parev

Ehida

Selamat Datang

Dia Dhuit

Hallo

And *Welcome*

Benjamin Zephaniah

Caterpillar's Lullaby

Your sleep will be

a lifetime

and all your dreams

rainbows.

Close your eyes

and spin yourself

a fairytale:

Sleeping Ugly,

Waking Beauty.

Jane Yolen

LIBRARY

No need even

To take out

A book: only

Go inside

And savor

The heady

Dry breath of

Ink and paper,

Or stand and

Listen to the

Silent twitter

Of a billion

Tiny busy

Black words.

Valerie Worth

SEASICK

"I don't feel whelk," whaled the squid,
   sole-fully.
"What's up?" asked the doctopus.
"I've got sore mussels and a tunny-hake,"
   she told him.

"Lie down and I'll egg salmon you,"
   mermaid the doctopus.
"Rays your voice," said the squid. "I'm a bit
   hard of herring."
"Sorry! I didn't do it on porpoise," replied
   the doctopus orc-wardly.

He helped her to oyster self onto his
    couch
And asked her to look up so he could
    sea urchin.
He soon flounder plaice that hurt.

"This'll make it eel," he said, whiting
    a prescription.
"So I won't need to see the sturgeon?"
    she asked.
"Oh, no," he told her. "In a couple of dace
    you'll feel brill."

"Cod bless you," she said.
"That'll be sick squid," replied the doctopus.

Nick Toczek

Who Says a Poem Always Has to Rhyme?

There was a young man called Frank
Who kept his pocket money in the ... *post office*

When he'd saved enough he bought an electric viola
And celebrated with a can of co...*conut cordial*

When he plays the viola the whole house rocks
It makes your shoes dance and it frightens your ... *granny*

Frank plays his viola all the time.
Who says a poem always has to ... *have the same sound*
at the end as it had at the end of the line before?

Roger Stevens

i want trainers

th@ stand out in the crowd

th@ mark u number 1 on the block

th@ raise u off the concrete

th@ stamp ur identity on the streets

th@ make every footstep a dance

th@ find their own way thru town

th@ magnetise the eyes of ur mates

with innersoles like trampolines

with tongues th@ reach ur knees

with laces th@ hang loose

with gold plated lettering

with treads deeper than tractor wheels

with footprints th@ spell danger

with hugely inflated price tags

coz my current ones r from the year dot

coz even sam has got a pair

coz feet need all the attention they can get

coz im suffering severe shoe envy

coz wot i wear is wot i am

coz style is my middl name

coz without branded footwear im a nobody!!!

silver

THE REV SPOONER'S SHOPPING LIST

Jaspberry ram

Chot hocolate

Ninger guts

Beggie vurger

Sea poup

Spixed mice

Lairy fiquid

Bea tags

Pushroom mizza

Chini meddars

Jackcurrant belly

Poo laper

Nicken choodles

Haghetti spoops

Lire fighters

Glubber roves

Sup a coup

Poothtaste

Palf a hound of Chensleydale wheese

and

Baked beans

(Gank thoodness)

Andy Seed

19

Mr Khan's Shop

is dark and beautiful.
There are parathas,

garam masala,
nan breads full of fruit.

There are bhajees, samosas, dhal,
garlic, ground cumin seeds.

Shiny emerald chillies
lie like incendiary bombs.

There are bhindi in sacks,
aaloo to eat with hot puris

and mango pickle. There's
rice, yoghurt,

cucumber and mint —
raitha to cool the tongue.

Sometimes you see
where the shop darkens

Mr Khan, his wife
and their children

round the table.
The smells have come alive.

He serves me
puppadums, smiles,

re-enters the dark.
Perhaps one day

he'll ask me to dine with them:
bhajees, samosas, pakoras,

coriander, dhall.
I'll give him this poem:

Sit down young man, he'll say,
and eat your words.

Fred Sedgwick

Little Girl, Be Careful

Little girl, be careful what you say

when you make talk with words, words –

for words are made of syllables

and syllables, child, are made of air –

and air is so thin – air is the breath of God –

air is finer than fire or mist,

finer than water or moonlight,

finer than spider-webs in the moon,

finer than water-flowers in the morning:

   and words are strong, too,

   stronger than rocks or steel

What You Say

stronger than potatoes, corn, fish, cattle,

and soft, too, soft as little pigeon-eggs,

soft as the music of hummingbird wings.

  So, little girl, when you speak greetings,

when you tell jokes, make wishes or prayers,

  be careful, be careless, be careful,

  be what you wish to be.

Carl Sandburg

THE CAR TRIP

Mum says:
"Right, you two,
this is a very long car journey.
I want you two to be good.
I'm driving and I can't drive properly
if you two are going mad in the back.
Do you understand?"

So we say,
OK, Mum, OK. Don't worry,
and off we go.

And we start The Moaning:
Can I have a drink?
I want some crisps.
Can I open my window?
He's got my book.
Get off me.
Ow, that's my ear!

And Mum tries to be exciting:
"Look out the window
there's a lamp-post."

And we go on with The Moaning:
Can I have a sweet?
He's sitting on me.
Are we nearly there?
Don't scratch.
You never tell him off.
Now he's biting his nails.
I want a drink. I want a drink.

And Mum tries to be exciting again:
"Look out the window
There's a tree."

And we go on:
My hands are sticky.
He's playing with the door handle now.
I feel sick.
Your nose is all runny.
Don't pull my hair.

He's punching me, Mum,
That's really dangerous, you know.
Mum, he's spitting.

And Mum says:
"Right I'm stopping the car.
I AM STOPPING THE CAR."

She stops the car.

"Now, if you two don't stop it
I'm going to put you out the car
and leave you by the side of the road."

He started it.
I didn't. He started it.

"I don't care who started it
I can't drive properly
if you two go mad in the back.
Do you understand?"

And we say:
OK Mum, OK, don't worry.

Can I have a drink?

Michael Rosen

INSTRUCTIONS FOR GIANTS

Please do not step on swing parks, youth clubs,

cinemas or skate parks.

Please flatten all schools!

Please do not eat children, pop stars, TV soap actors,

kind grannies who give us 50p.

Please feel free to gobble up dentists and teachers

any time you like!

Please do not block out the sunshine.

Please push all rain clouds over to France.

Please do not drink the public swimming pool.

Please eat all cabbage fields, vegetable plots

and anything green that grows

in the boring countryside!

Please do not trample kittens, lambs or other baby animals.

Please take spiders and snakes, ants and beetles home

for your pets.

Please stand clear of jets passing.

Please sew up the ozone layer.

Please mind where you're putting your big feet –

and no sneaking off to China when we're playing

hide-and-seek!

John Rice

A Dictionary of Snow

The Eskimos

have lots of words

for snow

There's fine snow

thick snow

blizzard snow

snow for building igloos...

Here's my list of words

for snow

splatty is for making snowballs

swoooosh is for sledging through

skolOSH is for kicking with your wellies

smooolly lies on the pavement

   waiting for footprints

shlumpish goes up and down over grassy fields

    until birds make patterns in it

squalOOM is to skid along in the playground

    before the caretaker throws sand on it

skulptush packs together squeaking in your hands

    as you build a snowman

I still need new words for the snow you wipe

off the tops of walls

as you run along the street

and for the sort that cakes

and melts on mittens

after a whole playtime

Rita Ray

Mystery

Where did it come from,

the idea of Human Beings:

people ... walking, talking, thinking,

who can run, write, reason.

People made of carbon and potassium,

more than 80% water

and with waterproof skin,

a jointed bone structure,

muscles, blood and a heart that is there,

beating, right from the start.

When did my heart begin?

And which came first...

the blood ... or the beat?

It's a mystery, all of it,

a mystery to me...

I wish I could have an idea

half as good!

Joan Poulson

A Boat in the Snow

On to the ocean's cold dark skin

Snowflakes are falling and are melting away.

How strange the snow seems out here!

How quickly the white blizzard is swallowed up

    by the waves.

Without the framework of land

Each flake's transformed.

Like a trillion ocean-borne moths

They flick into existence, then go.

As the sky above and around me

Glitters with frosty flecks of stars

So the deck of the boat glitters,

And I wonder, are whales sleeping

Out there in the world's depth beyond

The boat's bow? And I wonder,

Do they really sleep? And how?

There is no one to ask.

Snuggled up in cabins

Passengers are dreaming,

And all round us still the snow is falling,

And the ship's deck has become

A moonlit field, a field adrift

On the dark skin of the world.

I would love to sail forever between islands

of snow.

Brian Patten

First **Dog** on the **Moon**

"Hi there,

First Dog on the Moon,

How do you feel?"

Like nothing on Earth.

"Yes, but can you taste anything up there?"

Bones so cold and dry

They bite my tongue.

"That's great, First Dog on the Moon.

Now what can you smell?"

Fear of the things hiding in

Hard shadows.

34

"OK, OK, so what can you see?"

Long-dead forests,

Broken winds in empty streets,

Things,

Shadows.

"So what are you going to do next,

First Dog on the Moon?"

Sit and howl at the Earth.

David Orme

The Summer Day

Who made the world?

Who made the swan, and the black bear?

Who made the grasshopper?

This grasshopper, I mean –

the one who has flung herself out of the grass,

the one who is eating sugar out of my hand,

who is moving her jaws back and forth instead of up and down,

who is gazing around with her enormous and complicated eyes.

Now she lifts her pale forearms and thoroughly washes her face.

Now she snaps her wings open, and floats away.

I don't know exactly what a prayer is.

I do know how to pay attention, how to fall down

into the grass, how to kneel in the grass,

how to be idle and blessed, how to stroll through the fields,

which is what I have been doing all day.

Tell me, what else should I have done?

Doesn't everything die at last, and too soon?

Tell me, what is it you plan to do

with your one wild and precious life?

Mary Oliver

TABBY

My cat is all concentrated tiger.
I can only imagine the thousands
of millions of years
it must have taken to perfect her.
Growing smaller and smaller
with each evolution.
Growing more and more refined
and even-tempered under her fur.

See how she constantly licks
and grooms herself all over?

A small Queen of Sheba
stamping everywhere her padded
signature – a royal reminder
of the days she was a full-blown tiger.
Older O much older than Egypt.

Now, just look at her –
my grey and black tabby, stepping lightly,
emerging head first from between
the green grass stalks –

Ancient and new as the birth of a star.

Grace Nichols

Journey

I am the acorn

that grew the oak

that gave the plank

the Vikings took

to make a boat

to sail them out

across the seas

to England.

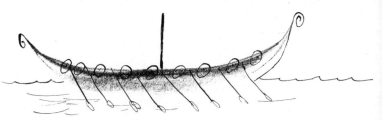

Judith Nicholls

Mapping Our World

The stream. Our special place,
In a tangle of woods
At the edge of the park.
It flowed through our childhood,
Ripple-voiced, light-darting,
With minnows in the shallows,
Mind-monsters in the deeps.
We followed it, mapped it,
Named its broads and narrows,
Its dams, falls and pools,
Waded, splashed, climbed, fished,
Knew the deep slow places under trees,
The soft mud that sucked at our legs,
The small Niagara where leaves rode the rapids,
The creaking branch, a bridge
For teetering tightrope-walkers,
The spangled green moss-cushion,
The lurking crocodile log.
We knew that scattered acorn-cups
Held drinks for fairies,

And that hazelnuts
Were nibbled by tiny teeth.
We knew the magic there
Would shimmer and dazzle
If only we could come by moonlight,
To see what crept from the mudbank
Abseiled from the trees
And danced in the shadows
Enchanting the fish.

While we whispered plans and secrets
The grown-ups shared flasks and gossip.
Answering their call, we came at last
Across the grass, wild with adventure,
Mud-streaked, moss-flecked, twig-snagged,
Story-mazed, stream-charmed,
And pitied them —

For their world
So much smaller than ours.

Linda Newbery

How Can I?

How can I *wind up* my brother

when I haven't got the *key*?

How can I **turn on** my charm

when I can't even find the **switch**?

How can I snap at my mother

when I'm not a crocodile?

How can I stir up my sister

when I'm not even holding a spoon?

How can I pick up my feet

and not fall to the ground on my knees?

How can I stretch my legs

when they're long enough already?

Parents! - They ask the impossible!

Brian Moses

The Unwritten

Inside this pencil
crouch words that have never been written
never been spoken
never been taught

they're hiding

they're awake in there
dark in the dark
hearing us
but they won't come out
not for love for time for fire

even when the dark has worn away
they'll still be there
hiding in the air
multitudes in days to come may walk
     through them
breathe them
be none the wiser

what script can it be
that they won't unroll
in what language
would I recognize it
would I be able to follow it
to make out the real names
of everything

maybe there aren't
many
it could be that there's only one word
and it's all we need
it's here in this pencil

every pencil in the world
is like this

W. S. Merwin

I Told a Lie Today

I told a lie today

and it curled up inside me

like a steel hard spring.

It was quite a clever lie,

no one guessed the truth,

they believed me.

But I've carried the twist of it

at the centre of my body, all day,

and I think it's expanding,

filling me up,

making my eyes feel red.

Perhaps it's going to uncoil suddenly

and burst me open,

showing everyone what I'm really like.

I think I had better confess,

before I'm completely unwound.

Robin Mellor

Ten **Things** Found in a **Wizard's Pocket**

A dark night.

Some words that nobody could ever spell.

A glass of water full to the top.

A large elephant.

A vest made from spiders' webs.

A handkerchief the size of a car park.

A bill from the wand shop.

**A bucket full of stars and planets,
to mix with the dark night.**

A bag of magic mints you can suck for ever.

A snoring rabbit.

Ian McMillan

Easy Money

Guess how old I am?
I bet you can't.
I bet you.
Go on guess.
Have a guess.

Wrong!
Have another.

Wrong!
Have another.

Wrong again!
Do you give in?

Seven years four months two weeks
five days three hours fifteen
minutes forty-eight seconds!
That's 20p you owe me.

Roger McGough

TRAVEL GENESIS

In the beginning was
the fin,
and fins were good,
for swimming.

When the fish finally
dragged itself out of the sea
on the crutches of its fins
it grew legs.

Four legs were very good,
for walking.
Two legs were better.
That made two arms.

Two arms made the wheel
and harnessed the horse.
Horse and wheel were very good,
for riding.

Horseless wheels were even better.
And so began:
the engine
the train
the car,
which were even better,
for riding.

In the end,
the engine sprouted wings,
excellent for flying,
and dragged itself off the earth:
first the aeroplane,
then the rocket ship,
giving birth to the Martian rover:

picking up a rock on an empty world
with a fin print on it.

Michael Lockwood

I'm Not Old Enough Yet

Even at three, this business of a big man

coming down the chimney loaded with pressies

from your list (who showed it to him?

Why wasn't he covered in soot?) seemed a bit

   far-fetched.

Especially since we didn't have a chimney.

But later I started to believe in this man

with the beard longer than God's.

I left food out. I tried to stay awake.

I still suspected Santa was a black woman dressed in red,

but I never, since three, asked my mum any questions.

Now I'm seven. A pal of mine asks, "Do you believe

in Santa Claus?" *What do you mean?* "Do you think

   it's true,"

she continued until my mouth fell open and I started

   to scream:

You shouldn't have told me. I'm not old enough yet.

Jackie Kay

From What Is the Truth?

O sing
Scupper-tyke, whip-lobber
Smutty-guts, *pot-goblin*
Garret-whacker, rick-lark
Sump-swab, *cupboard-adder*
Bobby-robin, knacker-knocker
Sneak-nicker, sprinty-dinty
Pintle-**bum**.

Ted Hughes

53

Hello, **MOON!**

Moon,
your reflection
is a tambourine
shaking
in the lake's ripples

You are the nightsong of the sun —
sometimes a full round note,
sometimes a high thin *plink*
plucked on a hidden guitar

Moon,
you have seen the dinosaurs
sleeping
in their fern beds —
Do you see me,
stretched beneath
my flowered quilt?

Moon,
did I ever tell you
that sometimes
(I'm sorry, moon, but...)

you look like a...
banana!

Patricia Hubbell

What the Wind Said

"Far away is where I've come from," said the wind.

"Guess what I've brought you."

"What?" I asked.

"Shadows dancing on a brown road by an old

Stone fence," the wind said. "Do you like that?"

"Yes," I said. "What else?"

"Daisies nodding, and the drone of one small airplane

In a sleepy sky," the wind continued.

"I like the airplane, and the daisies too," I said.

"What else!"

"That's not enough?" the wind complained.

"No," I said. "I want the song that you were singing.

Give me that."

"That's mine," the wind said. "Find your own."

And left.

Russell Hoban

One day while we were getting out our rough books

one day while we were getting out our rough books

there was a bit of a chattering

and Miss went all red and said stop stop **stop**

STOP STOP STOP

and we were very quiet

and Miss went more red and said

there is something the matter with the children

in class two purple

do you know what you are?

DO YOU KNOW WHAT YOU

and we were very very frightened

and we did not know what we were

John Hegley

ARE?

South to North: 1965

I was born south of the river
down in the delta, beyond the bayou
lived in the swamps just off the High Street
London alligators snapping my ankles.

It was Bromley, Beckenham, Penge, Crystal Palace
where the kids said *wotcha*, ate bits of *cike*,
the land my father walked as a boy
the land his father walked before him.

I was rooted there, stuck in the clay
until we drove north, moved to Yorkshire
a land of cobbles, coal pits and coke works,
forges and steel, fires in the sky.

Where you walked through fields around your village
didn't need three bus-rides to see a farm.

It was Mexborough, Barnsley, Sprotborough, Goldthorpe
I was deafened by words, my tongue struck dumb
gobsmacked by a language I couldn't speak in.

Ayop, sithee, it's semmers nowt
What's tha got in thi snap, chaze else paze?
Who does tha support, Owls else Blades?
Dun't thee tha me, thee tha thi sen
Tha's a rate 'un thee, giz a spice?

Cheese and peas, sweets and football
I rolled in a richness of newfound vowels
words that dazed, dazzled, danced
out loud in my head until it all made sense
in this different country, far away
from where I was born, south of the river

David Harmer

Moving In

A noisy street?

Yes, it was a noisy street

when we first arrived

and on the first night

I had to share a bed

with Geoff my brother

we couldn't find the other box of sheets

I didn't sleep at all

The trains over back

and the big vans echoing

echoing echoing

I thought I'd never sleep again

A cat cried

just like a baby

over and over again and

something knocked a dustbin over

Geoff so fast asleep

I've never felt so lonely

But in a week or so

your ears shut off

or else they get to like it

You'll see

it's not so bad

You'll get to know it all

just like your old place

near enough

Mick Gowar

GORAN

At the end of science,

No one could find Goran,

The new kid from Sarajevo.

Eventually, someone heard a sobbing

Coming from a cupboard

At the back of the room.

Miss opened the door

And there was Goran

Curled up inside.

Miss coaxed him out

And put her arm round him.

We filed quietly out to play,

Wondering what nightmares

The flames from our Bunsen burners

Had sparked inside

His war-scarred mind.

John Foster

65

The **Green** Bear

I am a **green** bear.

I do not dig a den like other bears,
Instead I build
A nest in a tree,
And climb to it at dusk,
And lie there while the mild winds
Rock me to sleep.

I am a **green** bear.

I do not eat berries or fish like other bears,
Instead I eat
Loaves of earth,
Which I set in the sun to dry
Until they're crunchy on the outside,
Sticky in.

I am a **green** bear.

I do not roar or snarl like other bears,
Instead I sing,
On moon-dark nights,
A short song
Like the foggy whistle
Of a distant train.

I am a **green** bear.

I am the colour of grass,
If I lay down in a field
You could walk
Straight by,
And not even know I was there.
It happens often.

I am a **green** bear.

I have **green** fur and a **green**
Heart and **green**
Meat on **green**
Bones, and I ask myself this question:
Am I the last in a long line of **green** bears
Or am I, perhaps, the first?

I am a **green** bear.

Richard Edwards

Haikus from Basho

1. In rainy weather
   even the cheeky monkey
   needs an umbrella.

2. From the ancient pond
   with a spring and leap and splash
   burps a new green frog.

3. When friends say goodbye
   forever, it's like wild geese
   erased by clouds

4. I gaze at the moon.
   Without the gathering clouds
   I would hurt my neck.

5. Tall summer grasses
   stand at ease now in the fields
   where the soldiers fell.

6. The pale butterfly
    gently perfumes her frail wings
    in an orchid bath.

7. This lonely poet
    walks down a long empty road
    into autumn dusk.

8. The morning after
    the night before, the firefly
    is only a bug.

Carol Ann Duffy

A Circus of Shapes

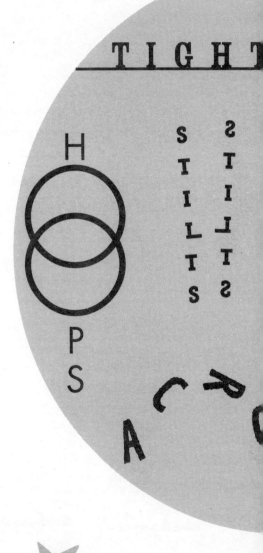

TIGHT

H

P
S

STILTS

STILTS

A

ROPE

CIRCUS

TRAMP LINE

A Y

B S

Gina Douthwaite

71

The Secret Place

It was my secret place –

    down at the foot

    of my bed –

    under the covers.

It was very white.

I went there

    with a book, a flashlight,

    and the special pencil

    that my grandfather gave me.

To read –

    and to draw pictures

    on all that white.

It was my secret place

    for about a week –

Until my mother came

    to change the sheets.

Tomie dePaola

"**M**"

My younger brother is learning his letters with my mum.

They're doing the "**M**" sound.

Mum says, "So,

how many words can you tell me

that begin with a "**M**"?"

And my younger brother says, "**M** for … mountain."

"Good," says Mum.

"**M** for … monster."

"That's right," says Mum.

"**M** for … magic."

"Well done!" says Mum. "Any more?"

*"And mummy begins with a **M**, too,"*

my younger brother adds, proudly.

"Of course!" says Mum.

"But do you know what Daddy begins with?" she asks.

"Yes," my younger brother says,

"A cough and a splutter every morning."

Graham Denton

Writing

and then i saw it

  saw it all   all the mess

and blood and everythink

 and mam agenst the kitchin door

 the flor all stiky

  and the wall all wet

and red an dad besid the kitchen draw

  i saw it saw it all

an wrote it down an ever word of it is tru

You must take care to write in sentences.
Check your spellings and your paragraphs.
Is this finished? It is rather short.
Perhaps next time you will have more to say.

Jan Dean

76

Poem 42

n

Othi

n

g can

s

urPas

s

the m

y

SteR

y

of

s

tilLnes

s

e. e. cummings

Why don't you...?

Why don't you join the choir?

Well, you have to sing on your own, don't you?

Don't be silly.
A choir means everyone singing together –
A chorus of voices.
Sometimes we sing hymns or carols,
Sometimes we sing songs – with ACTIONS!
We're in all the school concerts,
We sing to old people,
We take part in competitions,
We go all over – even to the cathedral.
We have a really good time.
You'd enjoy it.

OK. How do I join?

First, you have to sing on your own –

June Crebbin

78

The Laughter Forecast

Today will be humorous

with some giggly patches.

Scattered outbreaks of chuckling in the south

and smiles spreading from the east later.

Widespread chortling

increasing to gale force guffaws towards evening.

The outlook for tomorrow

is hysterical.

Sue Cowling

Stars

Stars

are to reach for,

beautiful freckles of hope,

speckles on velvet,

to steer ships,

to comfort those trapped in the darkness

    of their making,

to lead the wayward when the compass falters,

to remind us that the day is almost breaking,

dawn is just out – taking time to warm the other

    side of the world.

Stars are for wishes.

Stars are

tiny lights of hope,

fireflies in the night,

golden specks to gaze at,

tin tacks on a dark cloth,

studs glittering,

sequins on a first party dress.

Stars are

our brightest and best,

shards of hope to keep us going,

marking the place,

marking the seasons, giving us purpose

because somewhere out there

there are other star gazers

gazing back.

Pie Corbett

Wolf

A wolf is reading a book of fairy tales.

The moon hangs over the forest, a lamp.

He is not assuming a human position,

say, cross-legged against a tree,

as he would in a cartoon.

This is a real wolf, standing on all fours,

his rich fur bristling in the night air,

his head bent over the book open on the ground.

He does not sit down, for the words
would be too far away to be legible,
and it is with difficulty that he turns
each page with his nose and forepaws.

When he finishes the last tale
he lies down in pine needles.
He thinks about what he has read,
the stories passing over his mind
like the clouds crossing the moon.

A zigzag of wind shakes down hazelnuts.
The eyes of owls yellow in the branches.

The wolf now paces restlessly in circles
around the book until he is absorbed
by the power of its narration,
making him one of its illustrations,
a small paper wolf, flat as print.

Later that night, lost in a town of pigs,
he knocks over houses with his breath.

Billy Collins

ONE WORD WINTER POEM

Decemberrrrrr

William Cole

My **Mum** Says...

My mum says
she never left dirty socks under the bed,
made mashed potato mountains with gravy rivers,
stuck chewing gum under the table,
broke a plate and hid the pieces.

My mum says
she always did her homework before tea,
cleaned the hamster cage without being told,
brushed her teeth before she went to bed,
kissed her aunts without pulling faces.

My gran says
my mum has a very short memory.

Alison Chisholm

The Big Things

Early evening
I'm sitting in my favourite tree
gazing at the moon
in the pale summer sky
just thinking

Thinking about the big things:
like time
and infinity
and the cosmos
and how our little misty marble
of a planet
keeps spinning around
in that great murky soup
we call space

When Keith –
my next-door neighbour –
peers over the fence
and says "What you doin'
up there then?"

And I say
"Well, Keith – I was thinking
about the unstoppableness of time
and the smallness of me
and the wopping great bigness of space
and things."

And Keith says "Oh, right."

And I jump down
from the tree
climb over the fence
and say "Keith?
Do you ever think about time
and space and life
and what it all means and stuff?"

And Keith says "Fancy a game of footie?"

And I say "Do you, Keith?
And do you think about
how the planets all turn together
like the cogs of a massive cosmic clock?"

And Keith says "Look, you playing footie or
what?"

And I say "No seriously, Keith,
do you think about it?"

And Keith says "I'll go in goal."

And I say "Oh...WHATEVER."

James Carter

After the Book Is Closed

Whether it is the words

 or their meanings,

Or the sounds they make,

 or the way they echo one another;

Or simply the pictures

 they paint in the imagination,

Or the ideas they begin,

 or their rhythms...

Whether it's the words

 or their histories,

Their curious journeys

 from one language to the next;

Or simply the shapes they make

 in the mouth —

Tongue and lips moving,

 breath flowing.

Whether it's the words

or the letters used

To spell them, the patterns

they make on the page;

Or simply the way they call feelings

into the open

Like a fox seen suddenly in a field

from a hurrying train...

Whether it's the words

or the spaces between –

The white silences

among the dark print,

I do not know.

But I know this: that a poem

Will sing in my mind

long after the book is closed.

Gerard Benson

Oath of Friendship

Shang ya!

I want to be your friend

for ever and ever without
break or decay.

When the hills are all flat

and the rivers are all dry,

when it lightens and thunders
in winter,

when it rains and snows
in summer,

when Heaven and Earth mingle –

not till then will I part from you.

Author unknown, 1st-century China
Translated by Arthur Waley

It Is a Puzzle

My friend
is not my friend anymore.
She has secrets from me
and goes about with Tracy Hackett.

I would
like to get her back,
only do not want to say so.
So I pretend
to have secrets from her
and go about with Alice Banks.

But what bothers me is,
maybe *she* is pretending
and would like *me* back,
only does not want to say so.

In which case
maybe it bothers her
that *I* am pretending.

But if we are both pretending
then really we are friends
and do not know it.

On the other hand,
how can we be friends
and have secrets from each other
and go about with other people?

My friend
is not my friend anymore,
unless she is pretending.
I cannot think what to do.
It is a puzzle.

Allan Ahlberg

Two Plants

A plant called love.
A plant called hate.

I grew them both
in my garden.
The plant called love
was hard work.

All the watering
with tears of joy.
Not to mention the fact
that I talked to it.

The plant called love
ignored my words.
Or so it seemed.
It was in no hurry.

But the plant called hate
grew just like that.
I never fed it
or watered its roots.

Never spoke a word
to that plant called hate.
My thoughts were enough
to make it grow fast.

Will the birds be able
to tell the difference
when my plant called love
offers its slow green?

John Agard

Writing Poems

1: FREE VERSE

Most of the poems in *Orange Silver Sausage* are free verse.

A free-verse poem does not use rhyme. It does not have a regular rhythm in the way that a rhyming poem does. The rhythms of free verse are different from those of rhyming poems – softer, more subtle – and closer to the rhythms of prose and speech. Free-verse poems have a quieter music.

A free-verse poem uses fairly short lines and is chopped up into verses. It will often use repetition – see **Hello, Moon!** (p.54) and **My Mum Says...** (p.85). In **Hello, Moon!**, most of the verses begin with the same word – "moon". In **My Mum Says...**, each verse opens with the line "My mum says". Free verse also uses alliteration. This is when words begin with the same sound, for example "misty marble" (from **The Big Things**, p.86) and "boat's bow" (from **A Boat in the Snow**, p.32). Try using alliteration and repetition in your own writing.

Free verse is a wonderful form as it allows you to write in your own voice, with the language you use every day.

(If you are bilingual, you could weave both your languages into your poems.) Perhaps the most popular of all modern-day poets to write regularly in free verse is Michael Rosen. His poem **The Car Trip** is on p.24. He was inspired by other free-verse poets who also feature in this book, like e. e. cummings (see **Poem 42**, p.77) and Carl Sandburg (see **Little Girl, Be Careful What You Say**, p.22).

Poets often use free verse to write about their own lives, their memories, dreams, thoughts, imaginings and experiences. In one sense, it can be harder to write about these things in rhyme as you have to come up with good end-rhymes and the rhythm has to be tight. With free verse you can spend more time thinking about what you want to say, how you want to say it, and which words you really want to use.

Here are some subjects you might choose to write about:

★ A MEMORY: In **Mapping Our World** (p.40), the poet brings a memory to life by giving us vivid details – including "the soft mud" and "the creaking branch". Think of a place where you have played and bring it to life in a poem. But try not to put in too much detail – simple is best!

★ A CONVERSATION: **What the Wind Said** (p.56), **"M"** (p.74) and **The Big Things** (p.86) are poems told through conversations. Think of an interesting conversation you have had with someone. As with **The Big Things**, you could write the poem in the present

tense, as if it is happening right now, and you could begin
with "I'm sitting / talking / walking...".

★ AN AMAZING ANIMAL: See **The Green Bear** on
p.66. Write about your own colourful and fantastical creature. A blue wolf? A black lion? A red shark?

★ A SCHOOL STORY: See John Hegley's poem on p.58.
In only a few lines it tells of a dramatic event in class. Could
you do one like this?

2: A LIST POEM

A list poem is one that repeats a phrase, a word or a line
throughout (see **Stars**, p.80). You could try a list space poem
that repeats "The sun is...", "The moon is..." or "Jupiter is...".
i want trainers on p.16 is another list poem. You could
write your own version about something that you would like,
in a modern style – with no capital letters or punctuation.

3: A POEM THAT IS A LIST

What is simpler than to write a poem that is a short list of
things? Ian McMillan's **Ten Things Found in a Wizard's
Pocket** (p.48) is a modern classic. Who else might have a
pocket containing ten things? An alien? A ghost? A teacher?
An explorer? A time traveller? Try your own. Make sure the
last object is a good one to end on – something funny or
unusual or something to make your reader think.

Benjamin Zephaniah's **Greet Tings** (p.8), as the title suggests, is a list of greetings. Could you do your own? Try another phrase in as many languages as you can (research on the Internet for your words) – for example, "welcome" or "yes" or "happy birthday" or "happy Christmas".

The Rev Spooner's Shopping List (p.19) is yet another list. The Reverend Spooner was a man who really did get his birds all fumbled up. I mean words all jumbled up! Nowadays, words that are muddled up like this are called "spoonerisms". Could you do your own spoonerism poem – say a menu for Spooner's restaurant? Or a list of foods on special offer at Spooner's supermarket? Or Rev Spooner's Christmas list? Or Rev Spooner's favourite books or films?

4: HAIKU

See Carol Ann Duffy's haikus on p.68. A haiku is a three-line poem and each line has a set number of syllables. The word "poem" has two syllables: po-em. The word "elephant" has three: el-e-phant. How many syllables are there in your name? In a haiku poem, the first line has five syllables, the second line seven and the last line five. Haikus are perfect for capturing an image, a place or a snapshot in time. For instance:

On a frozen pond (5)
a small dog is nervously (7)
attempting to skate (5)

You could write about an animal, too, or a place – say, a beach in the early morning, a snowy forest, or the rain beating down on a busy street.

5: CALLIGRAMS

The poem **A Circus of Shapes** on p.70 is a calligram poem. A calligram is a word (or group of words) that has been made to look like what it means, for example – TALL, tiny and *curly*. Think of a set of words you can play with in this way. Would animal names work? Or types of sport? Or some verbs – "doing" words?

General Tips
for Writing Poems

★ Read everything and anything – not just poems, but non-fiction, novels, stories, plays, all kinds. The more you read, the more your writing will grow!

★ Read as a writer. Look out for tricks and things – even forms and styles of poems – that you can use in your own writing.

★ Keep a notebook or an old envelope with you for scribbling down ideas as they come to you.

★ Write about everyday things – your life, your thoughts, your family, your friends, your school.

★ Write down every idea and thought you have for the poem you are writing – even words or lines that might not seem to fit. You never know what you might want to use later.

★ Don't worry about getting your first draft perfect. With work later on, a rough first draft can turn into a very special second or third draft. As novelist Bernard Ashley says, "Don't get it right, get it written!"

★ Try to write on paper as much as you can. Roger McGough says working on the screen can make your work look too good too soon.

★ Don't be afraid to delete parts of your poem. Often in an early draft you can write too much – and less is nearly always more!

★ If the poem really wants to rhyme, that's fine – let it. But, more often than not, the best poems that young writers create are non-rhyming. You could always ask yourself the question "Am I rhyming for the sake of it? Would this poem be better if I took out the end-rhymes?"

★ Keep going! If you get stuck, leave it for a while – say a week or so. Then come back to it.

★ Show it to other people. Ask them for feedback. Ask them to read it out loud to you. Can you spot any areas that need more work?

★ Why not publish your poems? Try Poetryzone website – **www.poetryzone.co.uk** – or *Young Writer* magazine – **www.young-writer.co.uk**.

★ Try and write something every day. Get into the writing habit.

Performing Poems

Here are a few things you might want to think about before you perform a poem in front of an audience.

GET TO KNOW THE POEM REALLY WELL: Find a poem you really like. You could pick one from this book or one you have written yourself. Choose one that will work well in performance. Read it to yourself a couple of times. Then read it out loud a few times. Try and make sure you understand every word, phrase and line of the poem, and think:

   ♣ What do you like about the poem?

❀ What is it about?

❀ How does it make you feel?

❀ Why do you think it could be performed well?

MAKE NOTES: Take a photocopy of the poem. Jot down anything at all that will help you to perform it: (a) the sounds and the rhythms of the lines, and (b) any ideas you have about performance, such as actions and ways of using your voice. Have a think about:

❀ VOLUME/DYNAMICS: Vary the volume. Use soft/loud for specific words/lines/verses. You could speak softly for some parts of the poem and more loudly for others. But overall, is your voice loud and clear enough and – without your shouting – will the audience be able to hear you?

❀ PACE: Consider the speed. Try not to rush. Keep it nice and slow to start off with. Perhaps you could slow right down for the very last line – and even add an occasional pause – to build tension and suspense.

❀ MOOD/TONE: Is it a funny or serious poem or are there a range of moods? How can you can best express its feelings in your voice and actions?

INTRODUCE IT: Tell your audience the title of the poem. Maybe explain a little bit about why you chose it, and even suggest lines or actions they can join in on.

MEAN IT: Don't just say the words, mean them!

TRY IT: Experiment with different ways of performing the poem. Find out which is the most effective.

EXPRESS IT: Use actions, facial expressions, body movements, even eye contact – but don't overdo it ... the words are the most important bit!

RECORD IT: Then you can hear how it sounds, which might help you to develop your performance.

SHARE IT: Ask others to respond to your rehearsals.

LEARN IT: But keep a copy close by when you do the performance, just in case!

LIVE IT: Bring the world of the poem to life. Make the audience feel that they are inside the poem with you.

Clearly, the simplest way to perform a poem is ON YOUR OWN. However, you could do a solo performance and have a group or a whole class backing you – doubling up on lines or joining in for a chorus, or even adding actions. For example, if you were to do silver's **i want trainers** (p.16), you could perform the main poem yourself, and a "backing group" could double up or echo certain lines (even the two words "I want") – and do simple actions like pointing at their shoes. This poem could quite easily be performed as a rap, and would work well with clapping, beatboxing or percussion. Be careful not to drown out the words, though!

In a PAIR you could do alternate lines, phrases or words, or even use echo effects. You could double up for choruses – one performer could do actions while the other speaks. A poem such as **The Big Things** (p.86) is ideal for two voices. To prepare, you could discuss what props might be needed (a football, for instance), what actions you could do (the narrator could point at the sky whenever he mentions space) and how the two boys might act and speak.

In a SMALL or LARGE GROUP or even a WHOLE CLASS, individuals could take a line (or two) each and everyone could come together for the choruses, the final verse or certain lines. With poems like **Why don't you...?** (p.78) and **How Can I?** (p.42) it would be quite simple to give a line to each performer. One of you could introduce the poem. Then, one by one, each performer could do a line – perhaps coming forward, towards the audience, to say the line. With the poem **How Can I?** the actual words "How can I" could act as a "chorus" and everyone could join in at the start of each line. Try some actions too.

However you do your performance – on your own or with friends – just GO FOR IT!

Acknowledgements

'Some words I've studied for a time' Extract from 'Orange Silver Sausage' © Colin West. Reproduced by permission of the author. 'Greet Tings' from Talking Turkeys by Benjamin Zephaniah (Viking 1994). Copyright © Benjamin Zephaniah, 1994. Reproduced by permission of Penguin Group (UK). 'Caterpillar's Lullaby' © Jane Yolen, from Dragon Night and Other Lullabies by Jane Yolen. Reproduced by permission of Methuen. 'Library' from Small Poems Again by Valerie Worth. Copyright © 1986 by Valerie Worth. Reprinted by permission of Farrar, Straus & Giroux, Inc. 'Seasick' © Nick Toczek, from Where Sid the Spider Hid, a collection of creature poems by Nick Toczek (Caboodle Books 2008). Reproduced by permission of the author. 'Who Says a Poem Always Has to Rhyme?' © Roger Stevens. Reproduced by permission of the author. 'I Want Trainers' © Norman Silver. Reproduced by permission of the author. 'Mr Khan's Shop' © Fred Sedgwick, from Read Me: A Poem a Day for the National Year of Reading published by Macmillan Children's Books. Reproduced by permission of the author. 'The Rev Spooner's Shopping List' © Andy Seed, from The Poetry Store edited by Paul Cookson. Reproduced by permission of Hodder Children's Books. 'Little Girl, Be Careful What You Say' © Carl Sandburg, from Carl Sandburg: Poetry for Young People Series. Reproduced by permission of Sterling Juvenile US. 'The Car Trip' by Michael Rosen from The Hypnotiser (© Michael Rosen 1988) is reproduced by permission of PFDS (www. pfd.co.uk) on behalf of Michael Rosen. 'Instructions for Giants' © John Rice. Reproduced by permission of the author. 'A Dictionary